POKÉMON™

ULTIMATE QUIZ BOOK

ORCHARD

INTRODUCTION

Welcome, Trainer, to the wonderful world of Pokémon!

You've caught and traded rare Pokémon, met Mythical Pokémon and know the types of hundreds of fascinating species, but are you ready to take on an ultimate Pokémon challenge?

Get set to tackle quiz questions about Pokémon from every region that Ash and Pikachu have explored so far – from cute creatures in Kanto to new-found Galarian Pokémon.

There are true or false tests, multiple-choice quizzes, anagrams, picture puzzles and more. If you're seriously stumped, the answers are at the back of the book, but remember that a Pokémon champion never takes shortcuts.

Grab a pen and paper, then battle your friends to see who comes out on top! If you need any help, check out the official Pokémon Pokédex online at www.pokemon.com/uk

ALL ABOUT ASH!

Let's begin with a quiz about our epic hero, Ash. Good luck, Trainer!

1 How old is Ash?
- 9 years old
- 10 years old
- 12 years old

2 What is our hero's surname?
- Ketchum
- Pancham
- Kitchen

3 Which Pokémon did Ash want to be his first ever Pokémon?
- Sobble
- Squirtle
- Pichu

4 What type is Ash's first partner Pokémon?
- Ground
- Fire
- Electric

5 What is Ash's hometown called?
- Pallet Town
- Panda Town
- Party Town

6 Which region does Ash call home?
- Galar
- Kanto
- Hoenn

7 What is the first name of Ash's mum?

- ⊙ Deborah
- ⊙ Delia
- ⊙ Dolly

8 Who was the first Pokémon Professor Ash met?

- ⊙ Professor Birch
- ⊙ Professor Oak
- ⊙ Professor Maple

9 Which villainous team follows Ash through the regions?

- ⊙ Team Skull
- ⊙ Team Plasma
- ⊙ Team Rocket

10 What is Ash's mysterious ring from the Alola region called?

- ⊙ X-Ring
- ⊙ Y-Ring
- ⊙ Z-Ring

11 Ash first met a Scorbunny in which region?

- ⊙ Kanto
- ⊙ Alola
- ⊙ Galar

12 What was the first ever Pokémon that Ash caught?

- ⊙ Caterpie
- ⊙ Kakuna
- ⊙ Weedle

LEVEL UP!

Only top Trainers should attempt the next question...

CHAMPION TRAINER?

What is Ash's ultimate goal?

- ⊙ To complete his Pokédex
- ⊙ To become a Pokémon Master
- ⊙ To catch a Mewtwo

PREPARE FOR BATTLE!

These Pokémon are going head-to-head in battle!

Some Pokémon types are stronger against certain others. Decide which Pokémon has the best chance of winning each battle based on their type.

1

Grubbin
Bug

VS

Rookidee
Flying

2

Arcanine
Fire

VS

Wailord
Water

3

Corviknight
Flying – Steel

VS

Jolteon
Electric

4

Dusclops
Ghost

VS

Umbreon
Dark

5

Glaceon
Ice

VS

Grookey
Grass

6

Cottonee
Grass – Fairy

VS

Koffing
Poison

7

Lucario
Fighting – Steel

VS

Meowth
Normal

8

Pancham
Fighting

VS

Gardevoir
Psychic – Fairy

SIGNATURE MOVES

Which Pokémon is best known for performing the following moves in battle?

Choose one Pokémon from the opposite page to match to each signature move.

1 FURY SWIPES

2 SHADOW BALL

3 CONFUSION

4 WATER GUN

5 AURA SPHERE

6 VINE WHIP

7 DRAGON TAIL

8 FLAMETHROWER

TRAINER TEST

The Team Rocket tricksters are up to no good again – they are messing around with all the Poké Balls in the factory. Pick out the real Poké Ball in each row.

1
- Galactic
- Moon
- Planet

2
- Dive
- Wave
- Puddle

3
- Cure
- Heal
- Doctor

4
- Fine
- Great
- Strong

5
- Plant
- Leaf
- Safari

6
- Speed
- Quick
- Swift

7
- Nest
- Cave
- Burrow

8
- Luxury
- Treat
- Bonus

9
- Bucket
- Net
- Rod

10
- Ultra
- Mega
- Weak

HEADS AND TAILS

Work out who's who by studying the close-up pictures below.

Clue: all the Pokémon appear in the Kanto region.

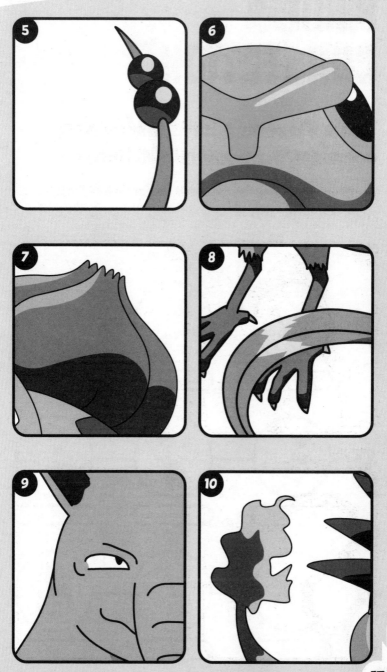

15

MAKE A CONNECTION

Some Pokémon have more in common than you might think!

Study each of the rows below carefully. Can you work out what connects the three Pokémon?

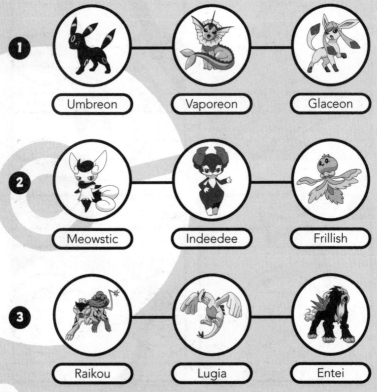

1 Umbreon — Vaporeon — Glaceon

2 Meowstic — Indeedee — Frillish

3 Raikou — Lugia — Entei

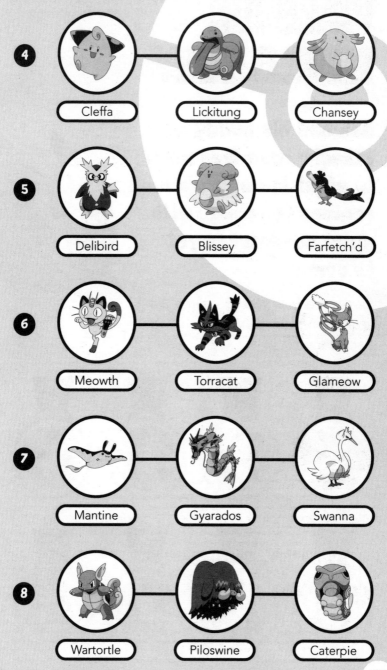

4 Cleffa — Lickitung — Chansey

5 Delibird — Blissey — Farfetch'd

6 Meowth — Torracat — Glameow

7 Mantine — Gyarados — Swanna

8 Wartortle — Piloswine — Caterpie

POKÉMON WORLD TOUR

Ash and his buddy Pikachu have travelled to eight known Pokémon regions together, with more adventures yet to come!

Earn a medal if you can name the regions in the order in which Ash visited them.

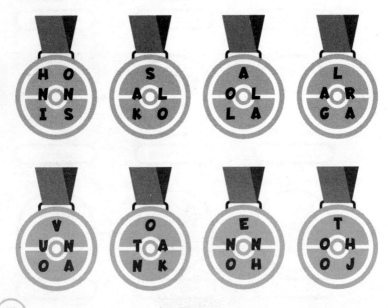

THAT'S THE PUFF!

Ash knows if he wants to keep Pokémon happy he can treat them to a delicious Poké Puff!

Test your Poké Puff knowledge by answering true or false to each question.

1 The main ingredient in Poké Puffs is Berries.

TRUE OR FALSE?

2 Poké Puffs come in eight delicious flavours.

TRUE OR FALSE?

3 There are six special Supreme Poké Puffs.

TRUE OR FALSE?

4 Poké Puffs come in strawberry flavour.

TRUE OR FALSE?

5 Humans and Pokémon alike gobble up these tasty treats.

TRUE OR FALSE?

6 While Ash loves to eat Poké Puffs, Pikachu is not a fan.

TRUE OR FALSE?

EEVEE'S EVOLUTIONS

Eevee may be a Normal-type Pokémon, but it's anything but ordinary!

This cute Pokémon can evolve into eight different evolutions. Name all of Eevee's evolutions and score a bonus point if you can name each Pokémon's type.

1

2

21

WINGED WONDERS

Only in Kanto might Trainers be lucky enough to catch a glimpse of one of the region's three Legendary birds. Can you unscramble their names?

1

O
N U
C I T
R A

2

T
R O
M E
L S

3

D
O   Z
P   A
     S

QUICK QUIZ

A Which one is an Electric- and Flying-type Pokémon?

B Which of the trio is a Flame category Pokémon?

C Which bird possesses a ribbon-like tail?

D Which Legendary is the smallest?

E Which has fiery wings and can heal itself in magma?

SIZE PRIZE

Test whether you've got the measure of these Pokémon.

Pick out the bigger Pokémon in each pair.

1 Pikachu OR Eevee

2 Pikachu OR Squirtle

3 Squirtle OR Cubone

4 Cubone OR Butterfree

5 Butterfree OR Cloyster

6 Cloyster OR Dewgong

7 Dewgong OR Kadabra

8 Kadabra OR Pinsir

9 Pinsir OR Slowbro

10 Slowbro OR Snorlax

CHAIN REACTION

Under the right conditions, many Pokémon will evolve into a new form.

Arrange these Pokémon from the Kanto region into the correct order of their evolution.

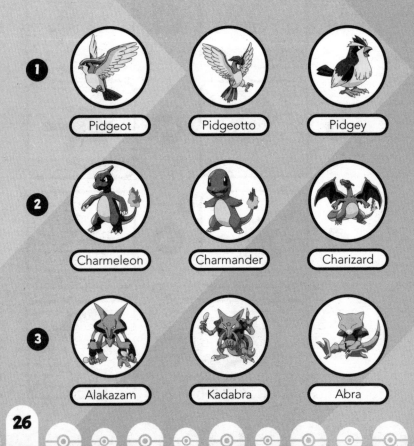

1. Pidgeot | Pidgeotto | Pidgey

2. Charmeleon | Charmander | Charizard

3. Alakazam | Kadabra | Abra

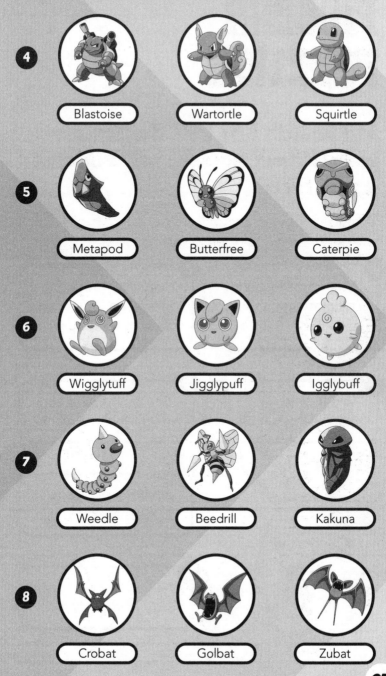

4
Blastoise · Wartortle · Squirtle

5
Metapod · Butterfree · Caterpie

6
Wigglytuff · Jigglypuff · Igglybuff

7
Weedle · Beedrill · Kakuna

8
Crobat · Golbat · Zubat

PIKACHU PUZZLERS

Ash wouldn't be half the Trainer he is without his true pal, Pikachu!

But how much do you know about our hero's best buddy?

1 What does Pikachu generate in its cheeks?

2 How can you tell whether a Pikachu is male or female?

3 Pikachu's tail is shaped like what?

4 Pikachu evolves into which Pokémon?

5 What type is Ash's companion?

6 Pikachu evolves from which Pokémon?

7 Name the two types of Pokémon that Pikachu is strong against in battle.

8 How do Pikachu greet each other – by shaking paws or touching tails?

9 True or false – Pikachu is also known as the Mouse Pokémon?

10 Which move can Pikachu not perform – Quick Attack, Tail Whip or Hydro Cannon?

Great going, Trainer! Now try this tough teaser...

CHAMPION TRAINER?

What can occur when several Pikachu gather together – lightning storms or earthquakes?

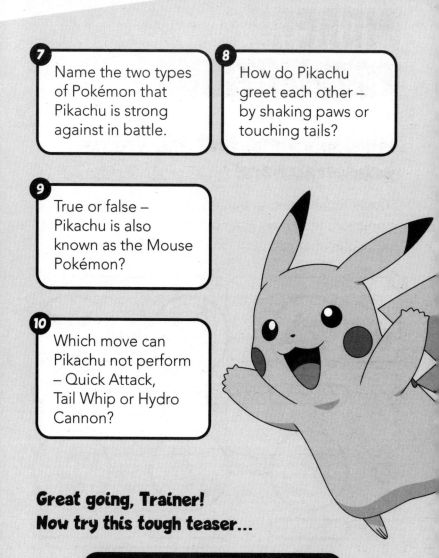

MORE CONNECTIONS

Here are some real headscratchers!

These Pokémon share a certain something in common. Study the rows below and see if you can work out what connects the three Pokémon.

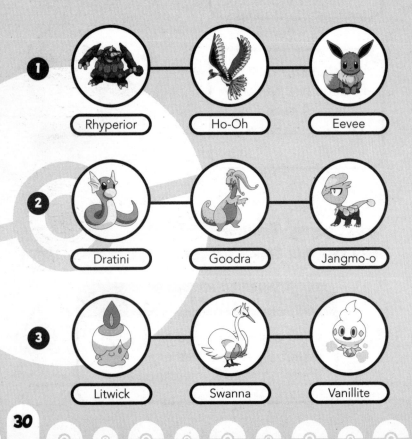

1. Rhyperior — Ho-Oh — Eevee

2. Dratini — Goodra — Jangmo-o

3. Litwick — Swanna — Vanillite

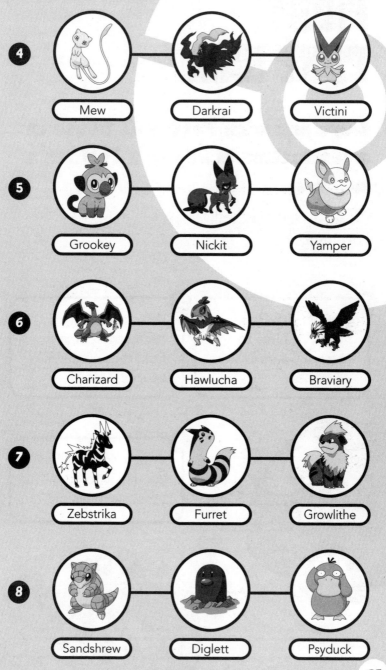

4 Mew — Darkrai — Victini

5 Grookey — Nickit — Yamper

6 Charizard — Hawlucha — Braviary

7 Zebstrika — Furret — Growlithe

8 Sandshrew — Diglett — Psyduck

PICK A POKÉ BALL

Knowing which Poké Ball to use in any situation is key to a Trainer's success.

Decide which Poké Ball is best to catch your Pokémon.

1 Which Poké Ball might you use to catch a Gyarados or a Scyther?

2 Which would you choose to catch a Pokémon that you'd caught before?

3 Which Poké Ball are you likely to have most supplies of?

4 What has a higher success rate than a standard Poké Ball?

5 What is the benefit of a Master Ball?

6 Which yellow-and-blue Poké Ball is better to use early in battle?

7 Which Poké Ball could be used to catch inexperienced Pokémon?

8 Should you use your Quick Ball at the start or end of a battle?

SMALL BUT MIGHTY!

Don't be fooled by these Pokémon, they may be small but they pack quite a punch!

Which ones have you caught?

(Pichu)　(Cleffa)　(Smoochum)　(Igglybuff)

(Elekid)　(Togepi)　(Magby)　(Tyrogue)

Now complete this quick quiz all about Johto's small but mighty Pokémon.

1 Which Pokémon's final evolution is Raichu?

2 Name a Pokémon that resembles a star?

3 Find the Fairy-type Pokémon that's said to bring good luck.

4 Which curious Pokémon uses its lips to show its likes and dislikes?

5 Which is the only Fighting-type Pokémon pictured?

6 Which Pokémon changes colour to yellow and orange when it evolves?

7 Which Pokémon generates electricity by spinning its arms?

8 Which Pokémon has a sweet scent?

THE PRIDE OF JOHTO

Johto region is home to five Pokémon that are rarely seen in the wild.

Use the shadows to help you identify each of Johto's Legendary Pokémon, as well as its type.

1

- **A** Psychic | Flying
- **B** Psychic | Fairy
- **C** Psychic | Water

2

- **A** Electric
- **B** Ground
- **C** Grass

3
A Water
B Ground
C Fire

4
A Fairy Flying
B Poison Flying
C Fire Flying

5
A Ground
B Rock
C Fire

CHAINS AGAIN

Can you find the evolution solution?

Sort the Pokémon below into the correct order they evolved.

Hint – each trio appears in the famous island region that is Hoenn!

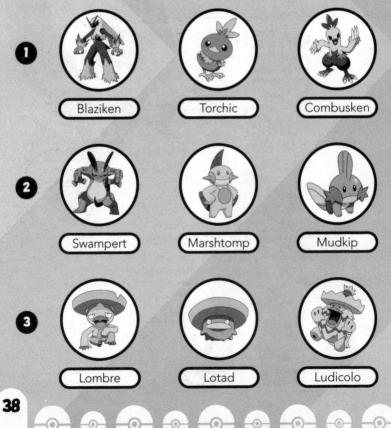

1 Blaziken   Torchic   Combusken

2 Swampert   Marshtomp   Mudkip

3 Lombre   Lotad   Ludicolo

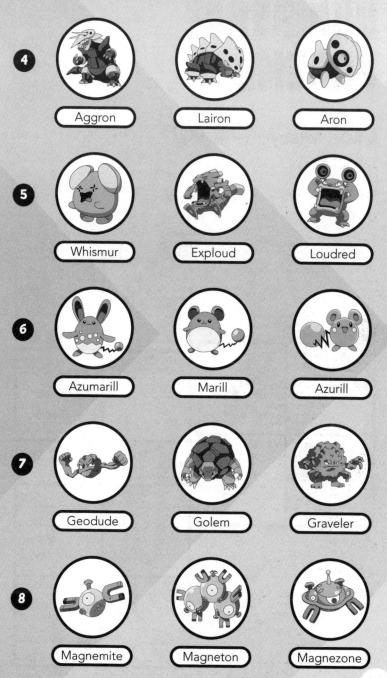

4
Aggron | Lairon | Aron

5
Whismur | Exploud | Loudred

6
Azumarill | Marill | Azurill

7
Geodude | Golem | Graveler

8
Magnemite | Magneton | Magnezone

NAME THAT POKÉMON!

Look sharp, Trainer!

Can you name the Pokémon in these picture mash-ups? Clue: they can all be encountered in snowy Sinnoh.

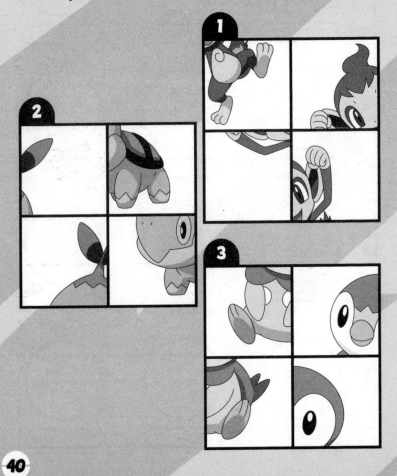

LEGENDARY POKÉMON

While travelling in the Sinnoh region, Ash discovered a host of mysterious Legendary Pokémon!

Pick out ONLY the Pokémon below that have Legendary status.

1. Azelf
2. Cresselia
3. Dialga
4. Bronzong
5. Giratina
6. Heatran

7 Mesprit

8 Palkia

9 Regigigas

10 Uxie

11 Arceus

12 Manaphy

13 Rhyperior

14 Shaymin

QUICKFIRE QUIZ

Set yourself a challenge by completing this speedy quiz, or test a friend's knowledge of these Pokémon found in Unova.

All you have to do is to name the main colour of each Pokémon. Try timing your attempt using a stopwatch!

1. Patrat
2. Pidove
3. Darumaka
4. Cottonee
5. Purrloin
6. Alomomola
7. Joltik
8. Duosion

9 Swanna

10 Pansage

11 Pansear

12 Tepig

13 Litwick

14 Lillipup

15 Ducklett

16 Snivy

17 Yamask

18 Trubbish

19 Vanillite

20 Stunfisk

21 Munna

22 Klang

23 Basculin

24 Chandelure

TOUGH TEAMS

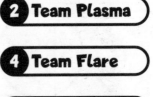

Team Rocket are not the only rivals that Ash has encountered on his quest to become a Pokémon Master.

In which region would you find the following teams?

1. **Team Skull**

2. **Team Plasma**

3. **Team Aqua**

4. **Team Flare**

5. **Team Magma**

6. **Team Galactic**

MYTH BUSTING

Three Mythical Pokémon are found in the Kalos region.

How well do you know the trio below? Separate the facts from the fiction.

1

Name:
(Diancie) **OR** (Diancis)

Category:
(Crystal Pokémon) **OR** (Jewel Pokémon)

Type:
(Psychic) (Fairy) **OR** (Rock) (Fairy)

2

Name:
(Holla) **OR** (Hoopa)

Category:
(Mischief Pokémon) **OR** (Merriment Pokémon)

Type:
(Psychic) (Ghost) **OR** (Psychic) (Steel)

3

Name:
(Volcanion) **OR** (Volcanoe)

Category:
(Steam Pokémon) **OR** (Lava Pokémon)

Type:
(Fire) (Water) **OR** (Fire) (Ground)

AMAZING ABILITIES

Pokémon in the Galar region never fail to amaze!

Each has its own talent, called an Ability. Decide which Pokémon from each pair possesses the Ability.

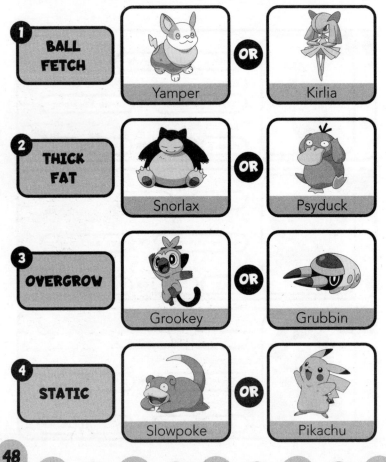

1 BALL FETCH — Yamper **OR** Kirlia

2 THICK FAT — Snorlax **OR** Psyduck

3 OVERGROW — Grookey **OR** Grubbin

4 STATIC — Slowpoke **OR** Pikachu

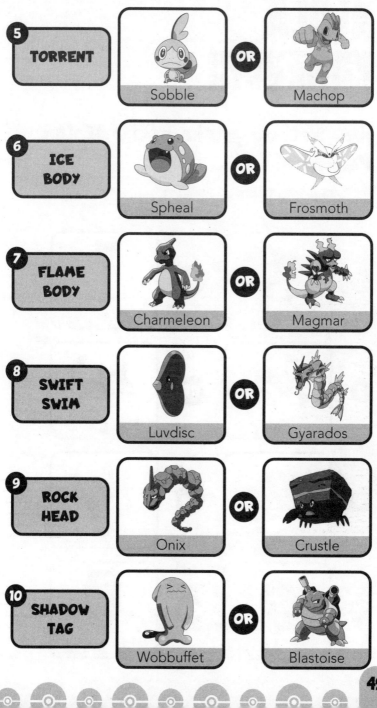

5 TORRENT
Sobble **OR** Machop

6 ICE BODY
Spheal **OR** Frosmoth

7 FLAME BODY
Charmeleon **OR** Magmar

8 SWIFT SWIM
Luvdisc **OR** Gyarados

9 ROCK HEAD
Onix **OR** Crustle

10 SHADOW TAG
Wobbuffet **OR** Blastoise

ALOLA FOREVER!

How well do you know the Alolan Pokémon?

Identify the Alolan form in each pair of Pokémon.

1. A **OR** B

2. A **OR** B

3. A **OR** B

4. A **OR** B

5 A OR B

6 A OR B

7 A OR B

8 A OR B

9 A OR B

10 A OR B

ISLAND LEGENDS

Did you know that each of the four main islands in the Alola region has a Guardian that fiercely protects its land and waters?

Study the shadows, then name the Legendary Guardian of each island.

1 Ula'ula Island

2 Melemele Island

3 Akala Island

4 Poni Island

HANG TEN

Here's a quiz that will test your knowledge of the first partner Pokémon that live in the Galar region. Try your best to score a perfect ten, Trainer!

1 How many first partner Pokémon exist in the Galar region?

2 Which first partner Pokémon carries a stick wherever it goes?

3 What type is Scorbunny?

4 What colour is Sobble?

5 Name the final evolution form of Grookey.

6 How many times can Scorbunny evolve?

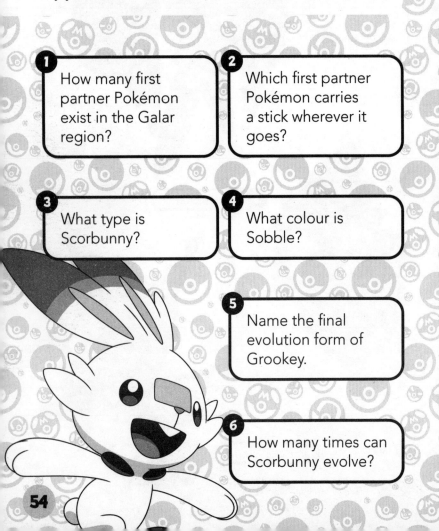

7 Which of the trio is weak to Water-, Rock- and Ground-type Pokémon?

8 True or false – Galar's first partner Pokémon are all the same height?

9 Which first partner becomes invisible when it gets wet?

10 Which Pokémon possesses the Blaze Ability?

FIRE 'EM UP!

Use the pictures to help you identify a dozen fiery Fire-type Pokémon that can all be found in the Galar region.

Ninetales

Scorbunny

Torkoal

Vulpix

Flareon

Charmander

Turtonator

Raboot

Sizzlipede

Torchic

Arcanine

Charmeleon

1. A fast Fire-type with juggling skills to boot.

2. Grabbing one of this Pokémon's many tails could result in a 1000-year curse.

3. Enemies should fear the explosive substances that coat this Pokémon's shell.

4. A friendly Pokémon with a flame-tipped tail.

5. This little Pokémon can 'torch' its foes!

6. A striped runner capable of covering thousands of miles each day.

7. Abandoned coal mines are full of these sooty Pokémon.

8. A sharp-clawed fighter with a scorching tail.

9. It wraps up its prey with its heated body, cooking them in its coils.

10. The Flame Pokémon into which Eevee evolves.

11. Special pads on this Pokémon's feet and nose radiate heat.

12. A fired-up Fox Pokémon with six tails.

TERRIFIC TRIOS

These Pokémon from Galar are proof that three heads can be better than one!

Can you identify these triple-headed creatures from their shadows?

MEGA EVOLUTION

With the help of a Mega Stone, Trainers can Mega Evolve certain Pokémon into extraordinary versions of themselves in battle.

Two of these Mega Stones are fakes – but which ones?

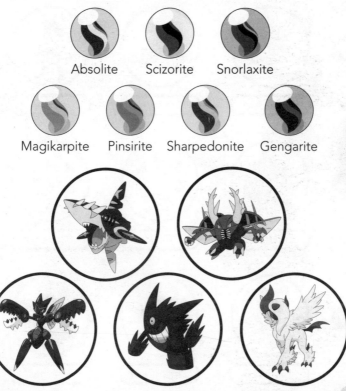

Absolite   Scizorite   Snorlaxite

Magikarpite   Pinsirite   Sharpedonite   Gengarite

ODD ONE OUT

One Pokémon in each row is different from the others.

Choose the odd one out and decide what makes it different.

1. Farfetch'd — Timburr — Lucario

2. Rhyhorn — Onix — Glaceon

3. Meowth — Zigzagoon — Gengar

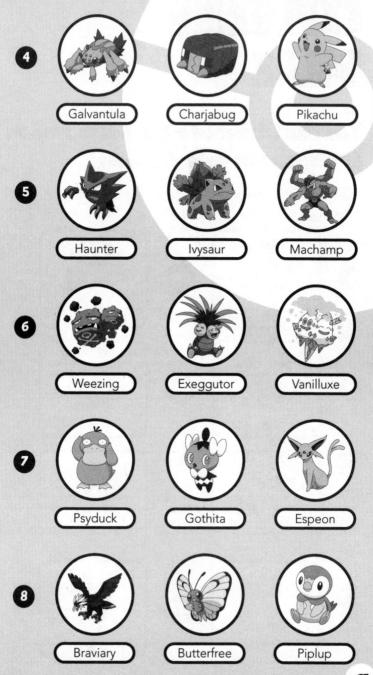

4
Galvantula | Charjabug | Pikachu

5
Haunter | Ivysaur | Machamp

6
Weezing | Exeggutor | Vanilluxe

7
Psyduck | Gothita | Espeon

8
Braviary | Butterfree | Piplup

EXPLORING GALAR

You must travel to the Galar region for this next quiz, Trainer!

Pick out the Galarian form from each Pokémon pair. Which version would you want to join your team?

1 A OR B

2 A OR B

3 A OR B

4 A OR B

HIGH VOLTAGE!

These Electric-type Pokémon that all appear in the Galar region know how to create a buzz!

Answer the questions below – use the picture clues if you get stuck.

1 Which is known as the Puppy Pokémon?

2 Charjabug is an Electric and which other type?

3 This Pokémon evolves from the treat-loving Yamper.

4 Eevee evolves into which Electric-type Pokémon?

5 Which Electric-type Pokémon is the category Stag Beetle?

6 A ball-shaped Electric- and Steel-type Pokémon.

7 Name the two Pokémon that Pikachu evolves from and into.

8 Name the venomous purple Pokémon that's a Poison- and Electric-type.

9 Lanturn evolves from which little Water- and Electric-type Pokémon?

10 A flat aquatic Pokémon that has a special Galarian form.

11 The Tiny Mouse Pokémon that can zap humans of any size.

12 Which Pokémon piggybacks onto other Electric types as it can't produce a charge on its own?

SCARY SQUAD

Team Rocket are far from a dream team, in fact they are the stuff of nightmares! How well do you know this villainous crew?

Take the quiz to find out.

1 What colour are Jessie's eyes?

2 What shade is James's hair?

3 What is the name of Team Rocket's big boss?

4 Whose Pokémon buddy do Team Rocket want to steal?

5 A shiny coin appears on the forehead of which member of Team Rocket?

6 What letter is emblazoned on the Team Rocket uniform?

7 Which member of the team comes from a rich family?

8 Why do they want to catch all the powerful Pokémon?

9 Which Normal-type Pokémon travels through the regions with Jessie and James?

10 In which region were Team Rocket associated with Bewear and Mimikyu?

KEEP NAMING THOSE POKÉMON!

Time for another eye test, Trainer!

Name the eight species in these mashed-up pictures. Clue: they can all be encountered in the green and pleasant land that is Galar.

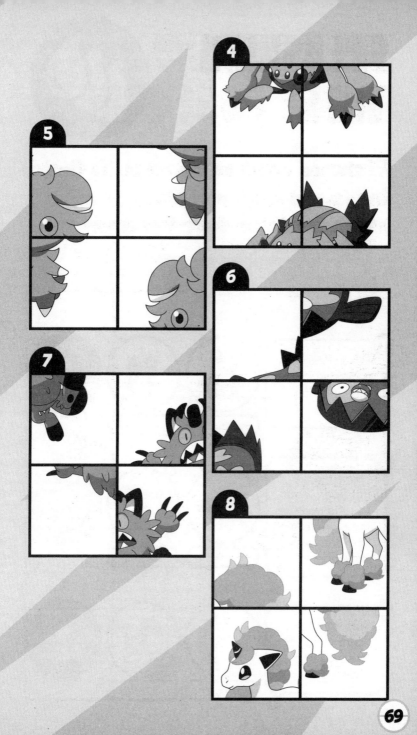

SPLASHING OUT!

It should come as no surprise that the island region of Galar is a haven to Water-type Pokémon.

How much do you about the region's aquatic inhabitants?

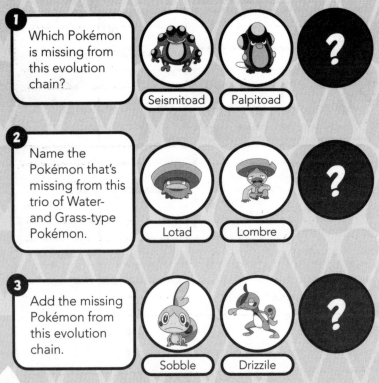

1 Which Pokémon is missing from this evolution chain?

Seismitoad | Palpitoad | ?

2 Name the Pokémon that's missing from this trio of Water- and Grass-type Pokémon.

Lotad | Lombre | ?

3 Add the missing Pokémon from this evolution chain.

Sobble | Drizzile | ?

4 Name the river-dwelling Pokémon that's the weakest in the Pokédex.

5 The skin of this Water Lizard Pokémon changes colour when it becomes wet.

6 A Water- and Flying-type Pokémon, its bill can carry Pokémon passengers.

7 A sly Water Lizard Pokémon that can squirt water balloons from its palms.

8 This winged wonder nests on sheer cliffs.

9 Which part of Kingler's body is oversized and prized in battle?

10 This Fish Pokémon is famous for needing little water to survive.

11 Which shelled Pokémon has jaws that can chomp through rods of steel?

12 Name the eight-legged Water-type Pokémon that sprays ink before attacking its prey.

LIGHTNING SPEED

The Galar region is host to a number of speedy Pokémon!

Check out the pictures and decide which critter is being described each time.

1 Which Pokémon can rapidly bore through the ground at 50 mph by squirming and twisting its massive body?

2 Known as the Drill King, this Pokémon can tunnel through the ground at speeds of over 90 mph.

3 Its mighty legs are capable of running at speeds exceeding 40 mph, but this Pokémon can only breathe underwater.

4 An Electric-type Pokémon that can easily hit 50 mph when running at top speed.

5 By rapidly rolling its legs, this little Rock- and Fire-type Pokémon can travel at over 18 mph.

6 A Dragon- and Ghost-type that is capable of flying faster than 120 mph.

Dracovish

Drakloak

Boltund

Onix

Carkol

Excadrill

FEATS OF HEAT

Talk about blowing hot and cold!

Study the pictures of Pokémon from the Galar region and work out which Pokémon is being described.

1 When it heats up, its body temperature reaches over 800 °C.

2 The temperature of the flames it breathes is almost 1,000 °C.

3 Anyone that bothers this Pokémon will be torched with flames that reach almost 1,500 °C.

4 Thanks to its icy scales, the temperature of this Pokémon's wings is less than -180 °C.

5 Once it has stored up enough heat, this Pokémon's body temperature can reach over 900 °C.

6 This chilly Pokémon blasts enemies with cold air reaching -100 °C, instantly freezing them solid.

Flareon

Frosmoth

Carkol

Vanillish

Centiskorch

Coalossal

DOUBLING UP

There's double trouble in the Galar region!

Look for Pokémon that have a double letter in their name – there are two pictured on these pages for each letter.

bb **pp** **oo** **rr**

nn **ee** **zz**

GO FURTHER!

Can you think of any other Pokémon with double letters that aren't pictured? They must all appear in the Galar region. There are plenty more – make a list!

EYE SPY

Do your sleuthing skills match detective Pikachu's?

Identify these Pokémon...
from only their eyes!

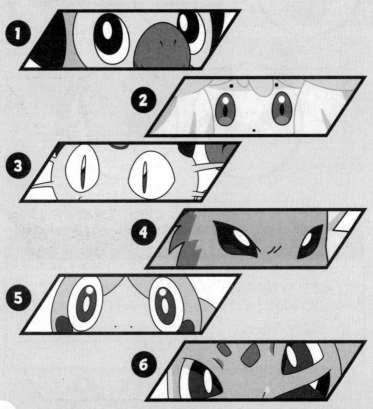

1

2

3

4

5

6

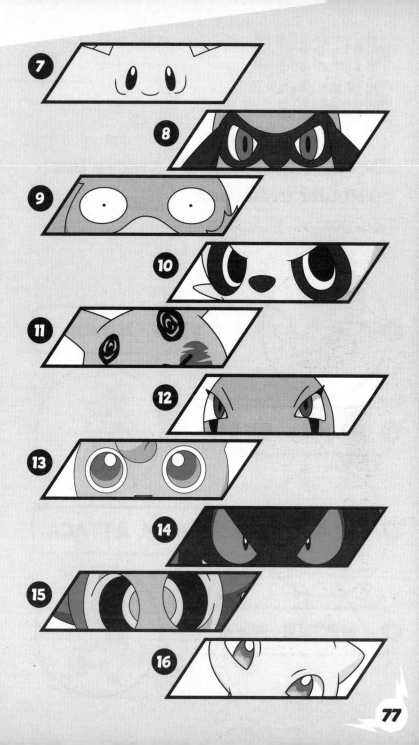

MISSING MOVES

Part of each Pokémon's move has been lost in battle!

List the missing words from all ten moves as quickly as you can.

1 VINE XXXX

2 XXXXX BEAM

3 XXXXX ATTACK

4 WATER XXX

5 XXXXX LEAF

6 FURY XXXXXX

7 XXXXXTHROWER

8 XXXXX PUMP

9 MIRROR XXXX

10 SHADOW XXXX

POWERFUL POKÉMON

The following Pokémon are strong and powerful!

Use your Pokémon knowledge to smash this quiz.

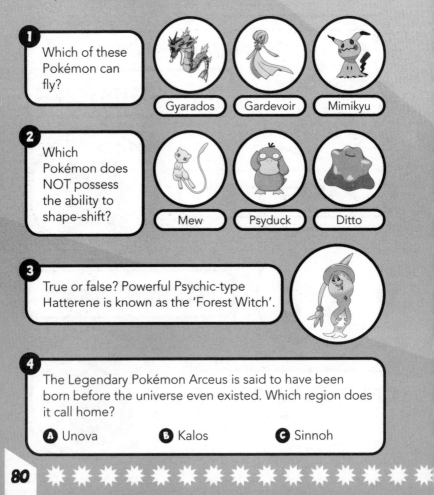

1 Which of these Pokémon can fly?

Gyarados

Gardevoir

Mimikyu

2 Which Pokémon does NOT possess the ability to shape-shift?

Mew

Psyduck

Ditto

3 True or false? Powerful Psychic-type Hatterene is known as the 'Forest Witch'.

4 The Legendary Pokémon Arceus is said to have been born before the universe even existed. Which region does it call home?

A Unova

B Kalos

C Sinnoh

5 Standing at a staggering 20 metres tall, Eternatus hails from which region?

6 This Pokémon needs only a single strike to fell even Gigantamax Pokémon. What is its name?

7 Where does Lugia, the mighty Flying- and Psychic-type Pokémon, live?

A Deep under the sea   **B** On a faraway island   **C** On a sheer clifftop

8 The rarely seen Mewtwo is a Legendary Pokémon. True or false?

9 Tyranitar's armoured body cannot be harmed by any sort of attack. The fighter combines which two Pokémon types?

10 A rare Dragon- and Flying-type. Meteoroids in its body provide the energy it needs to Mega Evolve. What is its name?

GALARIAN GREATS

Zacian and Zamazenta are found in the Galar region.

How much do you know about this Legendary pair?

1 Which of the two Pokémon is sometimes said to be older?

2 What type of Pokémon is Zacian Hero of Many Battles?

3 Which Pokémon was asleep for so long that people forgot that it ever existed?

4 Which Pokémon worked together with a king to save the Galar region in times past?

5 Name the Pokémon type for Zamazenta Crowned Shield.

6 Which is known as the Fighting Master's Shield?

7 Of the Legendary pair, whose markings are darker?

8 Which is taller – Zacian or Zamazenta?

9 Which Legendary is weak to Steel- or Poison-type attacks.

10 One Pokémon weighs significantly more than the other, but which?

FIGHTING TALK

This dirty dozen all talk tough and act tougher.

Answer the questions about Galar's Fighting-type Pokémon.

1 How many arms does Machamp possess?

2 What is the evolved form of Stufful?

3 Name the trio of fighters into which Tyrogue evolves.

4 What accessory is Timburr never seen without?

5 An honourable fighter, does Gallade use its blades for defence or attack?

6 Name Galar's flashy fighter known as the Wrestling Pokémon.

7 Pangoro is the evolved form of which Pokémon?

8 What symbol does Poliwrath bear on its chest?

9 Sawk's category is which martial art?

10 What colour are Riolu's eyes?

11 Toxicroak is a Fighting- and which other Pokémon type?

12 This Pokémon proves that six heads are better than one in battle. Name it.

LUCKY DAY!

Every Trainer needs a *little luck* on their journey and Togepi is one lucky charm that could help.

Tackle the seven questions that follow to see whether your luck is in!

 Name Togepi's type.

 True or false: Togepi's category is Happiness Pokémon.

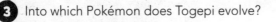 Into which Pokémon does Togepi evolve?

 True or false: Togepi's abilities are Serene Grace and Hustle.

 Is Togepi bigger or smaller than Pikachu?

 What is Togepi's shell said to be filled with?

 What is Togepi's final evolution form?

ANSWERS

ALL ABOUT ASH! Pages 6 - 7

1. Ten years old,
2. Ketchum,
3. Squirtle,
4. Electric,
5. Pallet Town,
6. Kanto,
7. Delia,
8. Professor Oak,
9. Team Rocket,
10. Z-Ring,
11. Galar,
12. Caterpie.

CHAMPION TRAINER:

To become a Pokémon Master.

PREPARE FOR BATTLE! Pages 8 - 9

1. Rookidee has the best chances of winning as Flying types are strong against Bug types (Grubbin).
2. Arcanine has the best chances of winning as Fire types are strong against Water types (Wailord).
3. Jolteon has the best chances of winning as Electric types are strong against Flying and Steel types (Corviknight).
4. Umbreon has the best chances of winning as Dark types are strong against Ghost types (Dusclops).
5. Glaceon has the best chances of winning as Ice types are strong against Grass types (Grookey).
6. Koffing has the best chances of winning as Poison types are strong against Grass and Fairy types (Cottonee).
7. Lucario has the best chances of winning as Fighting types are strong against Normal types (Meowth).
8. Gardevoir has the best chances of winning as Psychic and Fairy types are strong against Fighting types (Pancham).

SIGNATURE MOVES

Pages 10 - 11

1. Meowth,   3. Psyduck,   5. Lucario,   7. Dragonite,
2. Gengar,   4. Squirtle,   6. Bulbasaur,   8. Charmander.

TRAINER TEST

Pages 12 - 13

1. Moon,   4. Great,   7. Nest,   10. Ultra.
2. Dive,   5. Safari,   8. Luxury,
3. Heal,   6. Quick,   9. Net,

HEADS AND TAILS

Pages 14 - 15

1. Meowth,   4. Ninetales,   7. Bulbasaur,   10. Magmar.
2. Golduck,   5. Dragonair,   8. Articuno,
3. Raichu,   6. Caterpie,   9. Drowzee,

MAKE A CONNECTION

Pages 16 - 17

1. The Pokémon are all evolutions of Eevee,
2. The Pokémon have both male and female forms,
3. They are all Legendary Pokémon from the Johto region,
4. They are all pink Pokémon found in the Kanto region,
5. They all carry a food item,
6. Their Pokémon Category names involve the word 'Cat',
7. They are all Water- and Flying-type Pokémon,
8. Their names all end in the letter 'e'.

POKÉMON WORLD TOUR

Page 18

1. SINNOH, 2. KALOS, 3. ALOLA, 4. GALAR, 5. UNOVA,
6. KANTO, 7. HOENN, 8. JOHTO.

The correct order is: KANTO, JOHTO, HOENN, SINNOH, UNOVA, KALOS, ALOLA, GALAR.

THAT'S THE PUFF!
Page 19

1. True, 2. False – they only come in five flavours (with or without frosting), 3. True, 4. False, 5. True, 6. False – they both love them!

EEVEE'S EVOLUTIONS
Pages 20 - 21

1. Espeon – Psychic,
2. Flareon – Fire,
3. Glaceon – Ice,
4. Jolteon – Electric,
5. Leafeon – Grass,
6. Sylveon – Fairy,
7. Umbreon – Dark,
8. Vaporeon – Water.

WINGED WONDERS
Pages 22 - 23

1. ARTICUNO,	2. MOLTRES,	3. ZAPDOS.

QUICK QUIZ

A. ZAPDOS,	C. ARTICUNO,	E. MOLTRES.
B. MOLTRES,	D. ZAPDOS,

SIZE PRIZE
Pages 24 - 25

1. Pikachu – 0.4 m (Eevee is 0.3 m),
2. Squirtle – 0.5 m,
3. Squirtle (Cubone is 0.4 m),
4. Butterfee – 1.1 m,
5. Cloyster – 1.5 m,
6. Dewgong – 1.7 m,
7. Dewgong (Kadabra is 1.3 m),
8. Pinsir – 1.5 m,
9. Slowbro – 1.6 m,
10. Snorlax – 2.1 m.

CHAIN REACTION

Pages 26 - 27

1. Pidgey, Pidgeotto, Pidgeot.

2. Charmander, Charmeleon, Charizard.

3. Abra, Kadabra, Alakazam.

4. Squirtle, Wartortle, Blastoise.

5. Caterpie, Metapod, Butterfree.

6. Igglybuff, Jigglypuff, Wigglytuff.

7. Weedle, Kakuna, Beedrill.

8. Zubat, Golbat, Crobat.

PIKACHU PUZZLERS

Pages 28 - 29

1. Electricity, 2. Study the shape of its tail: straight = male, curved = female, 3. A lightning bolt, 4. Raichu, 5. Electric, 6. Pichu, 7. Water- and/or Flying-type Pokémon, 8. By touching tails, 9. True, 10. Hydro Cannon.

CHAMPION TRAINER:

Lightning storms.

MORE CONNECTIONS

Pages 30 - 31

1. Their names begin and end with the same letter,

2. They are all Dragon-type Pokémon,

3. White is the main colour of these Pokémon,

4. They are all Mythical Pokémon,

5. They all come from the Galar region,

6. They all have wings and can fly,

7. They all have a patterned coat,

8. They all only evolve once.

PICK A POKÉ BALL

Page 32 - 33

1. A Net Ball, as they are effective in catching Water- and/or Bug-type Pokémon, 2. A Repeat Ball, 3. The standard Poké Ball, 4. Great Ball, 5. It allows you to catch any Pokémon, 6. A Quick Ball, 7. Nest Ball, 8. At the start.

SMALL BUT MIGHTY!

Page 35

1. Pichu,   3. Togepi,   5.Tyrogue,   7. Elekid,
2. Cleffa,   4. Smoochum,   6. Magby,   8. Igglybuff.

THE PRIDE OF JOHTO

Pages 36 - 37

1. Lugia – a Psychic- and Flying-type Pokémon.
2. Raikou – an Electric-type Pokémon.
3. Suicune – a Water-type Pokémon
4. Ho-Oh – a Fire- and Flying-type Pokémon.
5. Entei – a Fire-type Pokémon.

CHAINS AGAIN

Pages 38 - 39

1. Torchic, Combusken, Blaziken.
2. Mudkip, Marshtomp, Swampert.
3. Lotad, Lombre, Ludicolo.
4. Aron, Lairon, Aggron.
5. Whismur, Loudred, Exploud.
6. Azurill, Marill, Azumarill.
7. Geodude, Graveler, Golem.
8. Magnemite, Magneton, Magnezone.

NAME THAT POKÉMON!

Pages 40 - 41

1. Chimchar,   3. Piplup,   5. Shinx,   7. Gastly,
2. Turtwig,   4. Kricketot,   6. Bronzor,   8. Sudowoodo.

LEGENDARY POKÉMON

Pages 42 - 43

1. Azelf, 2. Cresselia, 3. Dialga, 5. Giratina, 6. Heatran, 7. Mesprit, 8. Palkia, 9. Regigigas and 10. Uxie are all Legendary Pokémon. 11. Arceus, 12. Manaphy and 14. Shaymin are Mythical Pokémon, while 4. Bronzong and 13. Rhyperior are neither Mythical nor Legendary Pokémon.

QUICKFIRE QUIZ

Pages 44 - 45

1. Brown, 2. Grey, 3. Red, 4. Green, 5. Purple, 6. Pink, 7. Yellow, 8. Green, 9. White, 10. Green, 11. Red, 12. Orange, 13. White, 14. Brown, 15. Blue, 16. Green, 17. Black, 18. Green, 19. White, 20. Brown, 21. Pink, 22. Grey, 23. Green, 24. Black.

TOUGH TEAMS

Page 46

1. Alola, 2. Unova, 3. Hoenn, 4. Kalos, 5. Hoenn, 6. Sinnoh.

MYTH BUSTING

Page 47

1. Diancie, Jewel Pokémon, Rock- and Fairy-type;
2. Hoopa, Mischief Pokémon, Psychic- and Ghost-type;
3. Volcanion, Steam Pokémon, Fire- and Water-type.

AMAZING ABILITIES

Pages 48 - 49

1. Yamper, 2. Snorlax, 3. Grookey, 4. Pikachu, 5. Sobble, 6. Spheal, 7. Magmar, 8. Luvdisc, 9. Onix, 10. Wobbuffet.

ALOLA FOREVER!

Pages 50 - 51

1. B, 2. B, 3. A, 4. A, 5. B, 6. B, 7. A, 8. B, 9. A, 10. B.

ISLAND LEGENDS
Pages 52 - 53

1. Tapu Bulu, 2. Tapu Koko, 3. Tapu Lele, 4. Tapu Fini.

HANG TEN
Pages 54 - 55

1. Three, 2. Grookey, 3. a Fire-type Pokémon, 4. Blue,
5. Rillaboom, 6. Twice – into Raboot and Cinderace,
7. Scorbunny, 8. True, 9. Sobble, 10. Scorbunny.

FIRE 'EM UP!
Pages 56 - 57

1. Raboot, 2. Ninetales, 3. Turtonator, 4. Charmander, 5. Torchic,
6. Arcanine, 7. Torkoal, 8. Charmeleon, 9. Sizzlipede,
10. Flareon, 11. Scorbunny, 12. Vulpix.

TERRIFIC TRIOS
Page 58

1. Dugtrio, 2. Magneton, 3. Exeggutor, 4. Hydreigon,
5. Combee.

MEGA EVOLUTION
Page 59

The fakes are: Magikarpite & Snorlaxite.

ODD ONE OUT
Pages 60 - 61

1. Lucario – it doesn't carry anything, 2. Glaceon – the others
are mainly grey, 3. Gengar – the others have Galarian forms,
4. Pikachu is an Electric-type – the others are Bug- and Electric-
type, 5. Machamp – it is the only one that is a final evolution of
other Pokémon, 6. Exeggutor – the others have two heads,
7. Psyduck is a Water-type – the others are Psychic-type,
8. Piplup – it can't fly.

EXPLORING GALAR

Pages 62 - 63

1. B, 2. B, 3. A, 4. A, 5. A, 6. A, 7. A, 8. B, 9. A, 10. B.

HIGH VOLTAGE!

Pages 64 - 65

1. Yamper, 2. Electric- and Bug-type, 3. Boltund, 4. Jolteon,
5. Vikavolt, 6. Togedemaru, 7. Pichu and Raichu, 8. Toxel,
9. Chinchou, 10. Stunfisk, 11. Pichu, 12. Joltik.

SCARY SQUAD

Pages 66 - 67

1. Blue, 2. Purple, 3. Giovanni, 4. Ash's Pikachu, 5. Meowth,
6. The letter R, 7. James, 8. To create an army, 9. Meowth,
10. The Alola region.

KEEP NAMING THOSE POKÉMON!

Pages 68 - 69

1. Woobat,
2. Drednaw,
3. Alcremie,
4. Galvantula,
5. Espurr,
6. Stunfisk (Galar Form),
7. Meowth (Galar Form),
8. Ponyta (Galar Form).

SPLASHING OUT!

Pages 70 - 71

1. Tympole, 4. Magikarp, 7. Drizzile, 10. Feebas,
2. Ludicolo, 5. Sobble, 8. Wingull, 11. Drednaw,
3. Inteleon, 6. Pelipper, 9. Its pincer, 12. Octillery.

LIGHTNING SPEED

Page 72

1. Onix, 3. Dracovish, 5. Carkol,
2. Excadrill, 4. Boltund, 6. Drakloak.

FEATS OF HEAT

1. Centiskorch, 2. Carkol, 3. Coalossal, 4. Frosmoth, 5. Flareon, 6. Vanillish.

⊛ ⊛

DOUBLING UP

bb = Grubbin & Sobble, ee = Butterfree & Eevee,
nn = Bunnelby & Scorbunny, oo = Rillaboom & Wooloo,
pp = Applin & Flapple, rr = Espurr & Purrloin,
zz = Drizzile, Sizzlipede

GO FURTHER!

Other answers could include:

bb = Clobbopus, Dwebble, Krabby, Trubbish, Wobbuffet;

pp = Appletun, Copperajah, Grapploct, Hippopotas;

oo = Drifloon, Dubwool, Gloom, Grookey, Hakamo-o, Hoothoot, Kommo-o, Linoone, Obstagoon, Pumpkaboo, Raboot, Rookidee, Swoobat, Sudowoodo, Woobat, Wooper, Zigzagoon;

rr = Arrokuda, Barraskewda, Cherrim, Conkeldurr, Ferrothorn, Gurdurr, Karrablast, Perrserker, Timburr;

nn = Munna;

ee = Combee, Cottonee, Dreepy, Feebas, Goldeen, Greedent, Hitmonlee, Indeedee, Ribombee, Rookidee, Spritzee, Steelix, Steenee, Seedot, Tsareena, Orbeetle, Weezing;

zz = Mandibuzz, Salazzle.

⊛ ⊛

EYE SPY

1. Grookey, 2. Alcremie, 3. Meowth, 4. Jolteon, 5. Sobble,
6. Bulbasaur, 7. Togepi, 8. Riolu, 9. Psyduck, 10. Pancham,
11. Mimikyu, 12. Larvitar,13. Jigglypuff, 14. Gengar, 15. Duskull,
16. Mew.

MISSING MOVES

1. Vine Whip,
2. Hyper Beam,
3. Quick Attack,
4. Water Gun,
5. Razor Leaf,
6. Fury Swipes,
7. Flamethrower,
8. Hydro Pump,
9. Mirror Coat,
10. Shadow Ball.

POWERFUL POKÉMON

1. Gyarados, 2. Psyduck, 3. True, 4. c – Sinnoh, 5. The Galar region, 6. Zacian, 7. a – deep under the sea, 8. True, 9. Rock- and Dark-type, 10. Rayquaza.

GALARIAN GREATS

1. Zacian, 2. Fairy-type, 3. Zamazenta Hero of Many Battles, 4. Zamazenta Hero of Many Battles, 5. Fighting- and Steel-type, 6. Zamazenta, 7. Zamazenta, 8. Zamazenta – it is 2.9 m, Zacian is 2.8 m, 9. Zacian, 10. Zamazenta – it is 210 kg, Zacien is 110 kg.

FIGHTING TALK

1. Four, 2. Bewear, 3. Hitmonlee, Hitmonchan and Hitmontop, 4. A log that's three times its size, 5. Defence, 6. Hawlucha, 7. Pancham, 8. A spiral, 9. Karate, 10. Red, 11. Poison-type, 12. Falinks.

LUCKY DAY!

1. Fairy-type, 2. False – it's a Spike Ball Pokémon, 3. Togetic, 4. True, 5. Smaller, 6. Joy, 7. Togekiss.